Mamie
Eisenhower

Dwight D.
Eisenhower

PLATE 1

PLATE 2

PLATE 3

PLATE 4

PLATE 5

PLATE 6

PLATE 7

PLATE 8

PLATE 9

PLATE 10

PLATE 11

Do not
cut out
white area
between
arm and body.

PLATE 12

PLATE 13

Do not
cut out
white areas
between
arms and body.

PLATE 14

PLATE 15

PLATE 16